Casting the Dice

dice games and activities for children aged 5 to 11

Fran Mosley

ISBN 18 74099 83 9
Edited and typeset by Fran Mosley
Cover and illustrations by Andy Martin
Designed by Bookcraft, Stroud
Printed by Astral Printing, Stroud

CONTENTS

Games

Explorations

Collecting

you need   two 0–9 dice
         paper and pencil

Decide who is the Odd Person and who is the Even Person.

Here is what to do:

➤ Each of you, toss one dice

➤ Now add the two numbers together

➤ Decide whether the answer is odd or even

➤ If it is odd, that number belongs to the Odd Person; if it is even it belongs to the Even Person

➤ Write the number down; it is the score for this turn; in each turn, only one person scores

Keep running totals of your scores.

Go on playing until one of you has a score of 100.

Ann's dice   Sunni's dice

The total is 14; that's even.

Ann is the Even Person, so she gets 14 for this round and Sunni gets 0.

Variations

Use two 1–6 dice.

Finish the game
when someone reaches 50.

Try using other dice.

Start with a score of 100 and
subtract until you reach 0.

Questions

Who wins more often, the Odd
Person or the Even Person?

Why?

What are all the totals you can make
by adding the numbers on your dice?

How many of them are odd and how
many are even?

Diffy Dice

you need   four 1–6 dice

Starter person:

➤ toss two dice

➤ add up the dice-numbers to find your total

Other person:

➤ now **you** toss two dice

➤ add up the dice-numbers to find **your** total

The person who has the higher total wins this round. The score is the difference between the two totals.

The other person scores 0.

If your totals are the same, no-one wins that round.

Keep running totals of your scores.

Go on playing until one of you has a score of 30.

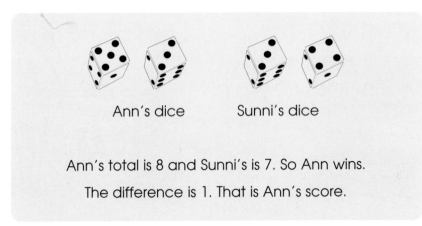

Ann's dice   Sunni's dice

Ann's total is 8 and Sunni's is 7. So Ann wins.

The difference is 1. That is Ann's score.

Variations

Use two 0–9 dice each.

The first person to reach a score of 50 wins.

One person tosses two dice and finds the difference between their numbers. Now the other person does the same.

The person with the bigger difference wins.

One of you, write down the numbers 0 to 10 on a sheet of paper.

Toss two 1–6 dice each. Now work out your totals, and find the difference.

Cross out that number on the paper.

Which numbers are really hard to score this way?

Why is that?

Questions

Toss two dice and find the difference between the numbers. What are all the differences you can get this way?

Same Aside

you need   six 1–6 dice

You need three dice each.

Each of you:

➤ toss your three dice and say what the numbers are

➤ if you get any numbers the same as your partner put those dice aside; you can't use those numbers

➤ add up your remaining numbers; that is your score for this round.

Keep doing this.

The first person to reach 50 is the winner.

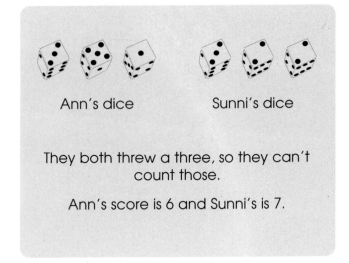

Ann's dice   Sunni's dice

They both threw a three, so they can't count those.

Ann's score is 6 and Sunni's is 7.

Variations

Start with a score of 50 and aim to reduce your score to 0.

Or start with 100 and aim to reduce it to 50.

Use 1–6 dice.

You mustn't count any dice-numbers which are thrown by both of you.

Each person adds up their other numbers and doubles them — that is their score for this round.

Aim for a winning score of 50, 100 or 200.

Questions

What are all the different totals you could get with three dice?

Which totals can you get in more than one way?

9

Make 300

you need   a 1–6 dice
paper and pencil

Draw three boxes for each person, all on the same sheet of paper. Write each person's name by their boxes.

Your aim is to write a three-digit number in the boxes, as close to 300 as you can get.

Decide who will start.

First person:

➤ toss the dice and say the number

➤ write that number in one of your boxes

Everybody takes turns like this until each box has a digit in it.

Read your three-digit numbers out loud.

Whoever's number is closest to 300 is the winner.

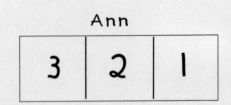

Ann

3	2	1

In her first go, Ann got a 2. She wrote 2 in her middle box.

In her second go she got a 1 and wrote it in her right-hand box.

In her third go she got a 3 and wrote 3 in her left-hand box.

Her number was 321 — and she was the closest to 300, so she won the game.

Variations

Score the difference between your number and 300 — and aim for a **high** score.

Draw two or four boxes each and make a two-digit or four-digit number.

Use a 0–9 dice and aim for 500 or 1000.

Play with three people.

When it is your turn you can write your dice-number in an empty box in **anybody's** grid.

This way you are involved in making other people's numbers as well as your own.

Allow one re-throw per person per game.

Toss 'em Again

you need   three 1–6 dice
pencil and paper

Decide who will start.

First person:

➤ toss all three dice and choose the highest number; set that dice aside

➤ toss the other two dice, and choose the higher number again; set that dice aside

➤ toss the last dice

➤ add up the numbers on your three dice; that is your score for this round

Everybody take turns like this. Whoever reaches 100 first is the winner.

12

Variations

Start with a score of 100 and aim to reduce it to 0.

Use three 0–9 dice.

Toss, toss and toss again, to get three numbers, as in the main game.

Now arrange your three numbers to make a three-digit number.

That is your score for this round.

6 **3** **1**

Aim for a winning score of 10 000.

Three in a Row

you need   two 1–6 dice
counters

In this game you are working together.

Your aim is to make a row of three counters. A row can go...

vertically, horizontally, or diagonally.

This is what to do:

➤ toss both the dice

➤ multiply the numbers you score together; you can use the grid to help you

➤ put a counter on the resulting number somewhere on the grid;

Keep going like this until you have made a line of three counters.

RULE

If, for example, you get a 3 and a 2, you can cover any of the 6s. It doesn't have to be where the 3 and 2 rows meet.

Ann tossed the dice and scored 2 and 2.

She multiplied these together to make 4.

She put a counter on the box where the 4 column met the 1 row.

1	2	3	●	5	6
2	4	6	8	10	12

×	1	2	3	4	5	6
1	1	2	3	4	5	6
2	2	4	6	8	10	12
3	3	6	9	12	15	18
4	4	8	12	16	20	24
5	5	10	15	20	25	30
6	6	12	18	24	30	36

Doubles and Trebles

you need   three 1–6 dice

Decide who will start.

First person:

➤ toss the three dice

➤ add dice-numbers together

➤ that is your score for this round (unless you get a double or treble as explained in the rules box)

Everybody takes turns like this.

The first person to reach 100 is the winner.

RULE

If you get two dice-numbers the same (doubles) you double your score for that round.

If you get three dice-numbers the same (trebles) you treble your score for that round.

16

Variations

If you don't have enough dice, you could use one dice and toss it three times.

Use four 1–6 dice and aim for 200.

If you get four dice-numbers the same, multiply your score for that round by 4.

Start with 100 and subtract your scores until you reach 0.

To 12 and Back

you need   three 1–6 dice
                 pencil and paper

Your aim is to write the numbers in order from 1 to 12, then cross them out.

Here is what to do:

➤ toss three dice and say the numbers

➤ write any numbers that the rules say you can

➤ go on tossing dice and writing numbers until you reach 12

When you reach 12 you have to go back to 1, this time crossing numbers out.

~~1~~ ~~2~~ 3 4 5 6 7 8 9 ~~10~~ ~~11~~ ~~12~~

> ## RULES
> You can't write any other numbers until you have thrown a 1.
>
> You MUST write the numbers in order.
>
> You can write numbers
> EITHER because one of the dice shows that number
> OR because you can make that number by adding or subtracting any of the dice-numbers

In his first go, Sunni got 1, 4 and 5.

First he wrote 1. Then he added 5 and 1, and subtracted 4 to get 2 ($5 + 1 - 4 = 2$).
So he wrote 2 as well.

18

Variations

You don't have to write the numbers in order.

Play with a friend.

Both of you take turns tossing the dice.

You must each try to write the numbers to 12, and cross them out, before your friend does.

Use three 1–12 dice and use them to write numbers up to 20.

You can use **any** operations to make the numbers.

Make 15

you need three 1–6 dice
pencil and paper

Your aim is to get as close as you can to 15 by adding your dice-numbers.

Decide who will start. When it is your turn, this is what to do:

➤ toss the three dice

➤ decide which, if any, of those numbers to keep; set them aside

➤ toss the remaining dice

➤ again, decide which, if any, of those numbers to keep; set them aside

➤ toss the remaining dice

➤ add up the numbers on your three dice and work out your score

Everybody keep taking turns like this.

Keep track of your score. The first person to reach 50 wins.

In her first go, Ann got 1, 5 and 3.
She decided to keep the 5,
and she tossed the other two dice again.

RULE

You don't have to have three tosses; you can stop earlier if you want.

SCORING

If you get	you score
15	15
13, 14, 16, 17	5
any other number	1

20

Variations

Aim for 5, not 15.

You **must** have three tosses, even if you like the dice-numbers you have already thrown.

Use four dice and aim for a different number.

You will need to invent your own scoring system.

(Will you allow four tosses as there are four dice?)

Use three 0–9 dice and aim for 20.

You will need to invent your own scoring system.

Number Snake

you need   two 1–6 dice
cubes or counters

The aim of this game is to cover up lots of numbers on the number snake. The higher the numbers, the better.

Here is what to do:

➤ toss the two dice

➤ use these two numbers, with one of these operations,

$$+ \quad - \quad \times \quad \div$$

to produce just one of the numbers on the snake

➤ cover up that number with a counter (if there is already a counter on that number, you can't put another one there)

Keep tossing the dice and making numbers to cover, until you can't cover a new number.

When that happens, the game is over. Work out what your score is.

SCORING

EASY VERSION

For every number under 10 you cover, score 5.
For covering 10, score 10
For every number over 10 you cover, score 15.

HARD VERSION

Add up all the numbers you cover. That is your score.

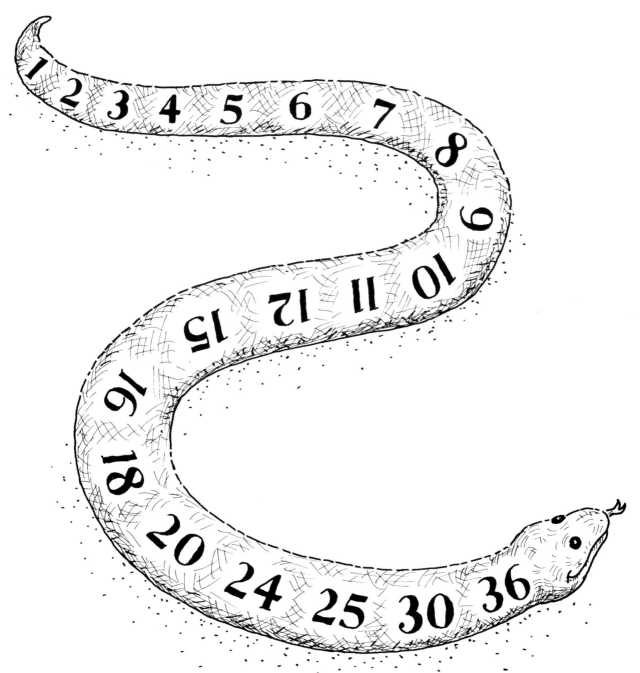

Pig

you need two 1–6 dice
pencil and paper

Your aim is to be the first person to reach 100. In each turn you want to get as high a score as you can, without going bust.

Decide who will start.

When it is your turn, this is what to do:

➤ toss both dice and add up the dice-numbers

➤ if the total is 6, your go is over and you score 0

➤ if the total is another number, write it down and decide whether to stop there or toss the dice again

Now go on playing according to the rules until your turn is over. Keep a note of the totals of all your dice-throws, and add them all up. That is your score for this turn, unless you get two dice-numbers that add up to 6 and go bust.

RULES

When it is your turn you can toss the two dice as often as you like — unless you get a total of 6, when you must stop.

If your two dice add up to 6, at any time, you go bust and your turn is over. You score 0 for this turn.

Otherwise, you can decide to stop the numbers on your turn whenever you like. Then your score for the turn is the total of all the dice-throws in that turn.

Keep a note of your scores. the first person to reach 100 is the winner.

24

Variations

For one person

Use two 1–12 dice.

You go bust if
the dice-numbers add up to
a multiple of 5.

Use whatever dice you
choose.

Maybe you could use three
dice.

Make up your own rule
about which numbers
make you go bust.

Mini-Pig

you need   a 0–9 dice
pencil and paper

Your aim is to be the first person to reach 100. In each turn you want to get as near to 20 as you can, but not go over.

Decide who will start.

When it is your turn, this is what to do:

➤ toss the dice as often as you like, and add up all the numbers you throw

➤ if you get to a total of 20 or more you **must** stop; otherwise you can decide when to stop

➤ now let the other person have a turn

Keep taking turns like this until somebody reaches a total score of 100.

RULES

When it is your turn you can toss the dice as often as you like — unless you get to 20 or over, when you must stop.

If your total for this turn is more than 20, you go bust and your turn is over. You score 0 for this turn.

Otherwise, you can decide to finish your turn whenever you like. Then your score for the turn is the total of all the dice-throws in that turn.

Variations

Use two 1–6 dice
or a 1–12 dice.

You aim for 30 and go bust
if your total reaches over 30.

Aim for 20 and use
two 1–6 dice.

You can use one or both
dice-numbers.

Use whatever dice you
choose. (What about using
three dice?)

Make up your own rule
about what number
to aim for.

Factors

you need   two 1–20 dice

In this game you are looking for factors. A factor is any number which divides exactly into another number. For example, 1 2, 3, 4 ,6 and 12 are the factors of 12.

Decide who will start.

When it is your turn, this is what to do:

➤ toss both the dice

➤ choose one of the numbers to be your Multiple Number

➤ work out all the factors of that Multiple Number

➤ add up the factors; the total is your score for this round (sometimes the only factors will be the number itself and 1)

Keep taking turns like this, and keep score. The first person to reach 100 wins the game.

| 2 | 15 |

Sunni threw 2 and 15. He chose 15 to be his Multiple Number.

The factors of 15 are 1, 3, 5 and 15. He added them together and got 24.

So 24 was his score for that turn.

Variations

A simpler version

Use two 1–12 dice and choose which number to have as a Multiple Number.

Aim for 50.

Use two 0–9 dice and multiply the numbers thrown to make your Multiple Number.

What happens?

Instead of tossing 1–20 dice, toss three 1–6 dice.

You can choose any of the numbers, or add two or three of them together to make your Multiple Number.

Aim for 50.

Properties

you need   a 1–20 dice
                counters in two colours

In this game your aim is to make a row of three counters in your colour.

A row can go...

vertically, horizontally, or diagonally.

Decide who will start. When it is your turn, this is what to do:

➤ toss the dice

➤ say the number

➤ look at the grid on the opposite page and choose a square that describes that number

➤ put a counter of your colour on that square

Keep taking turns like this until someone has made a line of three counters. They win.

14

Sunni threw 14. He thought about putting his counter either on 'even' or 'over 8'.

But then he decided to put it on 'next to a multiple of 3' (because 14 is next to 15, which is a multiple of three)

Variations

Instead of a 1–20 dice, use two 1–6 dice and multiply the numbers.

odd	multiple of 3	not an even number	greater than 5	over 8
even and over 10	between 10 and 20	has a 0 in it	square number	under 12 and over 5
multiple of 5	less than 8	under 10	12 or more	multiple of 4
next to a multiple of 4	odd and under 12	multiple of 6	even	under 15
multiple of 2	prime	has a 1 in it	more than 10	odd or even

Means

you need   two 0–9 dice
paper and pencil

In this game you use the calculator to help you find the mean average of your two dice-numbers.

Decide who will start.

When it is your turn, this is what to do:

➤ toss the dice

➤ find the mean of the dice-numbers by adding them up and dividing by 2

➤ that is your score for this turn

Keep taking turns like this. Keep a running total of your score.

Stop after ten turns each.

Variations

Use three dice.

Use two 1–6 dice, 1–12 dice, or 1–20 dice.

Investigations

Toss two dice repeatedly, and each time work out the average. Draw a graph of the results.

Now toss **one** dice repeatedly and draw a graph of the results.

Compare your two graphs. What do you make of them?

Try the same investigation with other dice.

Capture

you need   two 1–20 dice
three 1–6 dice
paper and pencil

In this game you each write down eight numbers, then try to capture each other's numbers.

First, take turns to toss the two 1–20 dice, add up the numbers, and write them down in a line or a list.

Do this eight times each, so that you each have eight numbers.

Now you can play the game. Decide who will start. When it is your turn, this is what to do:

➤ toss all three 1–6 dice

➤ use any of those numbers and any of these operations

$$+ \quad - \quad \times$$

to try to make **one** of your opponent's numbers

➤ if you can make one of their numbers, you capture it; they must cross it out from their list

Keep taking turns like this until one of you has captured more than half of your opponent's numbers. This person is the winner.

34

3 27 32 26 18 20 33 6

These are Sunni's numbers.

Ann tossed the dice and got 2, 3 and 6.

She did the calculation (3 × 6) + 2 = 20, and captured Sunni's 20.

He had to cross it out. Then it was his turn.

3 27 32 26 18 ~~20~~ 33 6

Questions

If Ann tosses the dice and gets 2, 3 and 6, what different numbers could she capture with them?

Aim for 50

you need   three 1–9 dice

Decide who will start.

Your aim is to get as close as you can to 50, by making a calculation with your three dice-numbers. You are allowed to toss your dice up to three times.

First person:

➤ toss all three dice, then

    1 decide if you want to stick with one or more of the numbers; if so set those dice aside

    2 (if you want to) toss the remaining dice; again decide which number or numbers to stick with and set those dice aside

    3 this is your last go; toss any remaining dice

➤ use your three dice-numbers to make a calculation; you can use any of these operations

      +   ×   −   ÷

Everybody take turns like this. Whoever gets closest to 50 is the winner for this round.

Play for ten rounds, and see who is overall winner.

RULE

You don't have to have three tosses; you can stop earlier if you want.

Sunni got 3, 4 and 6.

3   **4**   **6**

He did the calculation $(3 + 4) \times 6 = 42$

36

Variations

Aim to for a different number, not 50.

Your score in each round is the difference between your number and 50.

Whoever reaches a total score of 100 first **loses**.

Three Hops

you need   two 0–9 dice
pencil and paper

Toss both dice, read the numbers and put them together to make a two-digit number (either way round will do).

Write that number on your paper.

Now your aim is to get from that number to 100, or as close to 100 as you can manage, in just three hops.

Each hop consists of

● one of these operations

   + − × ÷

and

● a single digit

If you can't get to 100 exactly, try again with three different hops, starting at the same number.

Can you do it this time?

Sunni got 5 and 3. He put them together to make the number 53.

His first hop was '+ 7' and it took him from 53 to 60.

His next hop was '× 2'. It took him from 60 to 120.

His last hop was '− 9'. It took him from 120 to 111.

Then he went back to 53 and started again, to see if he could get to 100 exactly.

Simpler versions

Roll one dice and
write down the number.

Try to get from there to 50
in exactly three hops.

Use as many hops
as you like to get from
your number to 100.

Questions

Can you get from your number to
100 in two hops?

Which numbers work and which don't?

Is it true that you can get to 100
from any number under 10
in three hops or fewer?

Why? Prove it!

37   41   0   100

Aim for Zero

you need   a 1–6 dice
pencil and paper

Write 100 on your paper. That is your starting number.

Your aim is to reduce it to 0 by subtracting and dividing. You must stick with whole numbers — decimals aren't allowed.

Draw a waste bin at the bottom of your sheet of paper. You can put in there any numbers you don't want to use.

Now to start . . .

➤ toss the dice and look at the number

➤ decide whether to subtract that number, or divide by it, or whether to put it in the bin

➤ if you want to use it to reduce 100 to a lower number, do whichever calculation you choose (remember, no decimals);
if you don't want to use it, write it in the bin

Carry on like this until you reach 0.

How few goes do you need?

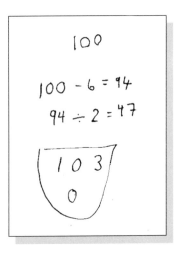

100

100 − 6 = 94

94 ÷ 2 = 47

1 0 3

0

Variations

Start at 0 and aim for 100

Use two 1–6 dice.

You can:

— add the two numbers and use the total, or

— just use one of them, or

— put them both in the bin

Collecting Data

you need   two 1–6 dice
pencil and paper

Toss the two dice and add up the dice-numbers.

Keep doing this. Make a record of what numbers you get, and how often you get them.

Make a graph to show your data.

What patterns can you see?

Which numbers are there most of? Which numbers are there fewest of?

Why?

Variations

Toss two dice and find the difference between the two numbers.

Make a record of what numbers you get, and how often you get them.

Make a graph of your data.

What patterns can you see?

Try tossing just one dice, or three dice.

What happens when you toss three dice and record just the middle number?

Is it different from what happens when you toss just one dice repeatedly?

The Mathematics Covered in the Activities

This chart gives you some idea of what mathematics you will be learning and practising when you do these activities and their variations

	Collecting	Diffy Dice	Same Aside	Make 300	Toss 'em Again	Three in a Row	Doubles and Trebles	To 12 and Back	Make 15	Number Snake	Pig	Mini-Pig	Factors	Properties	Means	Capture	Aim for 50	Three Hops	Aim for Zero	Collecting Data
properties of number	★												★	★					★	
place value				★																
decimals															★					
addition and subtraction to 20		★	★					★	★	★		★	★							★
addition and subtraction to 100	★	★	★		★		★		★		★	★	★		★	★	★	★	★	
addition and subtraction over 100				★	★		★													
multiplication and division						★		★		★			★			★	★	★	★	
doubling and halving						★														
averages															★					
probability				★					★	★	★	★		★	★					
reasoning about numbers	★			★		★		★	★		★				★	★			★	★
patterns and relationships						★							★	★						
handling data															★					★
working systematically		★	★					★					★			★	★		★	
working cooperatively	★	★	★	★	★	★	★		★		★	★	★	★	★	★	★			

Acknowledgements

BEAM would like to thank the following for trialling Casting the Dice, and for contributing ideas for games and activities:

Toni Ashman and Hazelwood Junior School, London

Frances Bestley and the South London Science and Technology Centre

Lin Bullard and Milwards CP School, Harlow

Muriel Chester and the Southwark BEAM Group

Peter Clarke, Primary Mathematics Advisory Teacher, London

Susan Cockroft and Bedwas Comprehensive School, Caerphilly

Shelagh Cosgrow and St Ursula's Infant School, Romford

Madeleine Donaher, Numeracy Advisory Teacher, Southwark

Lin Eager and Saltdean CP School, Brighton

Jean Edwards and The Avenue Infant School, Wellingborough

John Ellard and Wellsmead First School, Milton Keynes

Angela Folland and Our Lady & St Patrick's RC Primary School, Teignmouth

Mrs G Golden and Nutgrove Methodist Primary School, St Helens

Clive Harkcom and Verney Avenue School, High Wycombe

Sarah Herman and Oxhey Infant School, Watford

Karen Holman and Long Buckby Junior School, Northamptonshire

Val Jerram and the Brighton and Hove BEAM Group

Sue Lenihan and Broadmead Junior School, Croydon

Isabel McNaught-Davies and the East Sussex BEAM Group

Adèle Markey and Bury & Whitefield Jewish Primary School, Lancashire

Angela Perry, Ruth Webb and Okehampton Primary School, Devon

Vicki Price and South Tawton School, Devon

Penny Simkins and Somerton Primary School, Newport

Meredid Stone and Linda Thomas, Newport Borough Council Education Department

Ruth Trundley, Advisory Teacher for Mathematics, Devon

Debra Turner and Bevendean Primary School, Brighton

Lynda Waterhouse and St Jude's CE Primary School, London

Stephanie Whitcher and Chagford Primary School

The BEAM Development Group, Islington

Other books in this series

Calculators in Their Hands

by Fran Mosley

Ever heard someone say calculators make you lazy?

Well, it's not true. The calculator games and explorations in this book really stretch your mathematical powers — whether you are aged 6 or 60, 9 or 90. For instance, can you get from 0 to 22 in steps of 3? Or from 5 to 100 in just three stages?

Some of the games and activities are quite easy, and others are harder. But they are all fun. And you'll learn lots of mathematics in the process.

Calculators in Their Hands contains 23 games and activities for children, alone and with a companion, using calculators and everyday equipment such as pencils and paper.

Cards on the Table

by Fran Mosley

100 calculations in a minute!

Did you think that only computers could think that fast? You can do it too! (Well, nearly.) Playing these card games gets you doing all sorts of things with numbers — adding and subtracting them, working out factors, aiming for some numbers and avoiding others. The more you play them, the faster you become, and the more you develop your intuitive and flexible thinking skills — the mark of a real mathematician.

Cards on the Table contains 20 games for children to play with ordinary playing cards.

Numbers in Your Head

by John Spooner

How many numbers can you hold in your head?

The number games and investigations in this book will test your thinking powers and your memory. Can you add, subtract, multiply, divide, work out missing bits of sums, aim for target numbers and invent number patterns — all in your head?

This book, filled with brain teasers and puzzling investigations, challenges you to tackle all kinds of number problems. The more you exercise your mathematical thinking processes, the faster and more impressive your skills will become!

Numbers in Your Head contains 20 mental mathematics games and activities for children, alone or with a companion.